BRITISH ISLES

Edited by Claire Tupholme

First published in Great Britain in 2003 by
YOUNG WRITERS
Remus House,
Coltsfoot Drive,
Peterborough, PE2 9JX
Telephone (01733) 890066

HB ISBN 1 84460 202 8
SB ISBN 1 84460 203 6

FOREWORD

Young Writers was established in 1991 as a foundation for promoting the reading and writing of poetry amongst children and young adults. Today it continues this quest and proceeds to nurture and guide the writing talents of today's youth.

From this year's competition Young Writers is proud to present a showcase of the best poetic talent from across the UK. Each hand-picked poem has been carefully chosen from over 66,000 'Hullabaloo!' entries to be published in this, our eleventh primary school series.

This year in particular we have been wholeheartedly impressed with the quality of entries received. The thought, effort, imagination and hard work put into each poem impressed us all and once again the task of editing was a difficult but enjoyable experience.

We hope you are as pleased as we are with the final selection and that you and your family will continue to be entertained with *Hullabaloo! British Isles* for many years to come.

CONTENTS

Ewan Mackay	62
John Waters	63
Danna Wilson	64
Erin Flett	65
Kerri Cameron	66
Katy Berston	67
Ryan Norquoy	68
James Seatter	69
Steven Windwick	70
Ryan Kemp	71
Megan Foulis	72
Karen Laughton	73
Carolynn Leslie	74
Fiona Eunson	75
Jordan Yarrow	76
Amy Kerr	77
Claire McCreath	78
Astrid Nicolson	79
Erin Watts	80
Jenna Hamilton	81
Tina Griffiths	82
Laura Robertson	83

Quarff Primary School, Shetland Islands
Kirsten Jamieson	84
Dawn Smith	85
Lisa Manson	86

Rushen Primary School, Isle of Man
Glenn Watterson	87
Glenn Buckley	88
Gemma Toher	89
Emily Kelsall	90
Michael Craine	91
James Casizzi	92
Adam Brown	93
Lana Cowell	94
Jennifer Caley	95

The Poems

THE ISLE OF LEWIS

The small island of Lewis
Is completely surrounded by sea
Which roars and crashes against the rocks
When it's wild and stormy

The moor is covered in heather
Where the bleating sheep roam
Among the muddy peat banks
Where they wander to and fro

The blazing orange sun
On a beautiful summer's day
Shining on the golden beaches
Where the children like to play.

Lauren Macdonald (8)
Airidhantuim Primary School, Isle of Lewis

MY PET RABBIT

My cuddly pet rabbit called Snowy
Is white from head to tail
She loves to eat carrots and lettuce
And runs around in her pen

She has round pink eyes
And long fluffy ears
She digs holes with her paws
And gets her fur wet and dirty

She is very domesticated
And really rather tame
She loves to be stroked
By my sister and I.

Zoe Smith (8)
Airidhantuim Primary School, Isle of Lewis

MY CATS

My two cats, Tipsy and Sooty
Like to run about
Catching mice in our barn
Is their favourite pastime

When they come inside
They are sly and cheeky
Sneaking into Mum's bedroom
Biting and scratching the pillows.

Erin Offer (8)
Airidhantuim Primary School, Isle of Lewis

MY FAMILY

In my family there are six of us
Two sisters, one brother and me
It is hard work for my mum and dad
Keeping things peaceful and quiet

Jennifer and Caroline, my older sisters,
Just simply loving sleeping in bed
Never getting up when they are told
Driving Mum round the bend

Alexander, my little brother
Always hangs around my dad
They hammer and bang a lot
Giving us all a sore head.

Melanie Macdonald (8)
Airidhantuim Primary School, Isle of Lewis

MY CATS

My cute cat, Smoky
Is a fat, grey tabby
She chases her tail
And sleeps on my bed

My fluffy cat, Indie
Has dark, glossy fur
He digs his sharp claws
Into my bedroom carpet

Sooty, my oldest cat
Is eight years old
His bones are very sore
But he can still catch mice.

Kathleen Morrison (8)
Airidhantuim Primary School, Isle of Lewis

MY FAMILY

My dad is funny and kind
He always tells me jokes
When I come home from school
He is waiting with milkshake and toast

My mum is always organising
When she gets home from work
She tells me to wash the dishes
And calls me for my tea

I have an older brother
Warren is his name
He listens to music on his CD
And watches programmes on TV

My grandpa sometimes has a snooze
In his big comfy chair
He makes me hot chicken soup
On a cold winter's day.

Connor Mackay (8)
Airidhantuim Primary School, Isle of Lewis

MY PETS

I have ducks and hens
They're all in their pens
Dogs, cats, horses and rats
They're all in their cages
But cleaning takes ages.

There are hundreds of fish
In one *big dish*
There is Goldie and Billy, Cracker and Milly
They all live in one big dish.

We do have some owls
Wrapped up in towels
They fly at night
And even in light.

We do have gerbils
We do have mice
And out in the shed
There are even some *lice!*

There are some cows
There are some sheep
There are some bats
That are always asleep.

Ceitlin Lilidh Russell Smith (10)
Airidhantuim Primary School, Isle of Lewis

THE STORM

We had a storm
It was really bad
We couldn't go outside
It was really sad.

Aaaaaaah!
I hate that sound
I hate that light
It gave me a fright.

There was some thunder
There was some rain
There was some lightning
Oh, what a shame!

The last flash was red
So I ran to bed
I got back up again
Into my den.

Kirsty Maclean (11)
Airidhantuim Primary School, Isle of Lewis

ANIMALS

The alligator snaps its jaws,
The crocodile clicks its claws,
Parrots and sparrows fly ahead,
Eagles and crows whoosh behind,
Flamingos and robins, budgies too,
A barn owl loudly hoots - *'Tu-whit tu-whoo!'*
Lions and cheetahs, they are big cats,
Unlike pet cats, they roar instead.
Frogs and dogs, rats and cats,
Toads and birds, snakes and lizards,
There are lots of farm animals -
Cows, sheep, horses and pigs.
Fishes in their shoals,
Eels dig holes,
Fish with shining scales,
Unlike dolphins and whales.

Animals, animals, they're so great,
All of them, they're like my mates!

Sandra Corbett (9)
Airidhantuim Primary School, Isle of Lewis

ME

I'm sometimes happy, sometimes sad
I'm sometimes thoughtful, sometimes glad

I'm sometimes kind and careful
I'm sometimes tired and rough

I sometimes start to daydream
When life is just too much

I'm sometimes bored and sleepy
After a long day's toil

I'm sometimes good at stories
I'm sometimes slow at work

But the only thing I care about
Is my lovely island home.

Fiona Rennie (10)
Airidhantuim Primary School, Isle of Lewis

PIGGY

My little piggy is so sweet
But not everyone agrees,
They think he's rude and ugly,
Especially when he'll sneeze.

He is so cute and loving
And that is what I like,
Just because he's pink and porky,
I won't tell him to take a hike.

He does snorting noises
Which can sound funny,
That's just my little piggy
He is a pig, not a bunny!

So that is my piggy
Who loves to get mucky,
So what, I love him dearly
And I think I am very lucky.

Heather Donnelly (9)
Airidhantuim Primary School, Isle of Lewis

THE GOAL

Together we are the best
We put our opponents to the test
Five boys playing to win
As the whistle blows we begin.

The whole school cheers us on
As James kicks the ball, wide and long,
To the ground it bounces at my foot
So I give it a great, thumping boot.

Off the post the ball rolls back
The opponents are now on the attack
Defenders are ready to intercept
But the goalie in the air has leapt.

Now we are determined to score
The crowd gives a great big roar
Passed to me the ball I get
So I hit the ball to the back of the net.

Kevin Matheson (10)
Airidhantuim Primary School, Isle of Lewis

DOLPHINS

D ocile friendly mammals
O rdinary they are not
L oving to all they meet
P erfect as they swim
H igh in the air they jump
I n and out of hoops
N oisy squeaks they make
S kin as smooth as silk.

Gemma Macdonald (9)
Airidhantuim Primary School, Isle of Lewis

ANIMALS OF THE WORLD

A   ll God's creatures
N   ot one the same
I   ndia's elephants with floppy ears
M onkeys swinging branch to branch
A   lligators wallowing in the mud
L   ong snakes slithering through the grass
S   ome in the water

O   ctopuses with all their legs
F   ish with the funny gills

T   he sharks slicing through the sea
H   ippopotami swimming in the mud
E   erie bats in caves

W olves hunting in the night
O   striches running wild
R   obins sitting in the summer trees
L   ions with their pride
D   olphins leaping in the air.

Amanda Mitchell (10)
Airidhantuim Primary School, Isle of Lewis

NUMBERS

Numbers, numbers, all around
Numbers, numbers, I have found
Numbers, numbers, can make up money
Numbers, numbers, can be very funny
Numbers, numbers, you can measure
Numbers, numbers, give you pleasure
Numbers, numbers, make you dizzy
Numbers, numbers, can put you tizzy
Numbers, numbers, you can add
Numbers, numbers, how old is Dad?
Numbers, numbers, can make you glad
Numbers, numbers, can make you mad
Without numbers we'd be lost
However could we count the cost?

Peter John Macdonald (11)
Airidhantuim Primary School, Isle of Lewis

THE STORM

Rain lashing against the window
Lightning flashing in the sky
Am I safe in my bed
As the storm goes by?
Rolling thunder frightens me
Oh stormy nights are very long
Am I safe in my bed
As the storm rages on?
As finally it begins to calm
Whistling and howling quietens at last
I am safe in my bed
And the storm has passed.

Conner Macdonald (9)
Airidhantuim Primary School, Isle of Lewis

MY FRIENDS

My friends are important to me
Because they are always there you see
They help me when I fall
And when I start to bawl
They play with me when I'm sad
And don't leave me feeling bad
They like the same things I do
That means lots of fun and games too
I think in the end
It's great to have friends.

Alasdair White (10)
Airidhantuim Primary School, Isle of Lewis

I WONDER

I wonder why I grow so tall
And why my sister is so small?

Why do the winds dance around?
Why don't they walk on the ground?

I wonder how the stars stay up in the sky
And how the thunder rocks on high?

Why is it that people believe in magic
Instead of solving situations which are tragic?

I wonder if that noise at night is a mouse
As it softly creeps around my house?

Why do I want to stay in bed
When the rain patters on the window above my head?

I wonder why my heart misses a beat
Before a race till the finish line I meet?

I wonder if my mother knows
And would she tell me, do you suppose?

Kathryn Offer (10)
Airidhantuim Primary School, Isle of Lewis

SPACE

Look at the planets everywhere
Jupiter, Saturn and Mars
All part of the galaxy
With the constellation stars.

The sun, centre of the solar system
A vast ball of fire in the sky
You can see it from far away
If you stood on it, you'd fry.

The moon is a huge ball of rock
Which on Earth can be seen at night
When the blazing sun shines on it
It looks like a bright light.

Travelling into space
An astronaut I'd like to be
Floating above the world
Everything I'd see.

Andrew Omand Taylor (9)
Airidhantuim Primary School, Isle of Lewis

THE MONSTER

The monster is very, very hairy
He is also enormous and quite scary
When he roars people run away
And never come back to play.

A big green bulging eye
Makes all the children cry
Green, slimy skin as bright as a lime
Shining, but more gruesome than grime.

His tail is so long and furry
He smells as if he always eats curry
His horns are as sharp as a knife
If he got near you it would be the end of your life!

Johnathan Macleay (9)
Airidhantuim Primary School, Isle of Lewis

MY HOMEWORK

Dear Teacher,
I did not hand in my homework today,
Because I was far, far away,
I got abducted by aliens,
And they took my homework.
Then I landed in Norway,
The aliens kept my homework,
So I had to do it again!
Then, a bird took it away,
So I had to do it again!
Then I was walking to school
And it blew away,
A car made it all muddy,
I was late for school,
So I had to leave it,
Oh what a shame!
Oh, Teacher, one more thing,
Can I try again?

Jade Smales (10)
Burray Primary School, Orkney Islands

EXCUSES FOR MY HOMEWORK

Oh, I'm so sorry, Teacher, my dog ate my homework
So I wrote it out again.
Then a warthog took it to a supermarket.
Then an old lady stole it and hobbled away.
Then the lady's cat gobbled it up!
There was no paper left in the house.
All the shops were closed
(Because it was Sunday)
So I could not write it out again.
Really it is not a lie!
Oh, I forgot to say about the fly!

Kelsi Watt (9)
Burray Primary School, Orkney Islands

I'M AS...

I'm as strong as a boulder,
As gentle as a fly,
As fast as a sidewinder,
As slow as a poker,
As happy as a smile,
As silly as a joker,
As jumpy as a monkey,
As tall as Mount Everest,
As imaginative as a dream,
As hot as lava,
Yes, that's me!

Ethan Prior-Sanderson (8)
Burray Primary School, Orkney Islands

Miss!

My dog ate my homework!
My mum, she told him off
So I just typed it out again!
But on my way to school,
A spaceship landed right beside me
And took my homework away,
Luckily I had a copy!
But, Miss . . .
When I was just at the gate . . .
The wind just blew my homework
Right down the street,
I chased it, Miss, I really did
But it went down the drain,
Which is why my homework will be late . . .
I'll try again tomorrow.

Belinda Banks (10)
Burray Primary School, Orkney Islands

EXCUSES

Dear Teacher,
My homework is going to be late,
I wrote my homework
but the cat ripped it up.
So I wrote it again
but the rabbit chewed it all up.
So I wrote my homework again
but a parrot flew away with it.
I did my homework again
Before I went to school
But this time when I was walking to school,
The wind blew my homework out of my hand.
I tried to catch it
but the wind blew it up too high,
so I promise to bring it in tomorrow.

Cheryl Smith (8)
Burray Primary School, Orkney Islands

MY PET

I once had a pet tiger,
Who growled at everyone he saw.
He was as big as four tyres . . .
I don't know if he was a tiger after all!

He might have been a lion,
The mighty king of the jungle,
Or maybe even a cheetah,
The fastest animal in the world.

It all came to an end
When I sold him to the zoo . . . saying,
'I am sure he will be
     happy with you.'

After all that
I bought a dog for a pet.
I told him to roll over
But he did a poo instead!

Alasdair MacLennan (8)
Cliasmol Primary School, Isle of Harris

A FRIGHTENING CREATURE

It has laser-sharp teeth
And bright green eyes.
Four legs - no hands and
Really strong thighs.

It has a huge mouth
And a tiny nose
Webbed feet
So you can't see his toes!

His knees almost reach
His big fat chin.
He is poisonous - but shy
And you couldn't call him thin!

His tongue is long
(To catch his food).
He eats flies
And thinks they're good!

He's ugly and green
And eats lots of grog
I hope you don't meet
This strange-looking . . . frog!

Sara McCombe (11)
Cliasmol Primary School, Isle of Harris

WHY US?

Why us?
Me and my cubs,
Setting fire to a tree,
Oh how dare they?
Burning and smoke all around,
Devastation around,
Our homeland destroyed,
Why us?
The fire crackling,
Me and my cubs are spluttering,
We're roaring like mad,
Sparks hitting us,
The fire swallowing the trees,
Why us?
People running in our way,
I'm sprinting as fast as I can,
My cubs leaping,
Trying to stay near me,
Why us?
One of my cubs has got lost
In the flames,
The other, by my side dying,
Nothing I can do,
For I'm only a tiger,
Oh why us?

Emma-Jane MacAskill (10)
Dunvegan Primary School, Isle of Skye

JEOPARDY

Everything is silent
in the
rainforest.
Animals, people and
birds
are gathering up
their herds.
Suddenly it starts,
devastation,
chaos.
Trees are burning
fast,
fast,
fast,
People running
quick,
quick,
quick,
Thick smoke hovers
in the air.
People coughing stop
and stare.
Miserable people lie
in their beds
breathing the air that's
polluted and dead.

Hannah Lee Dinneen (9)
Dunvegan Primary School, Isle of Skye

THE SKY

The sun shines brightly in the sky
Giving us heat and light
The moon shines brightly in the night
Giving us light at night.

Caitlin Barnett (7)
Murray's Road Junior School, Isle of Man

THE SUN

The sun is big and shiny
It lights up all the sky
Although the moon will come to night
The sun will never die.

Sarah Quine & Abbi Belloir (9)
Murray's Road Junior School, Isle of Man

THERE ONCE WAS A BOY FROM SURREY

There once was a boy from Surrey,
Who liked to eat lots of curry,
He ate and he ate,
Until was his fate,
He rushed to the loo in a hurry!

Melissa Dove (11)
Murray's Road Junior School, Isle of Man

THE HORRENDOUS TROLL

Be wary of the mouldy troll
that diner lies in wait
to drag you to his dingy hole
and put you on his plate.

His blood is bad and scorching hot
he rudely moans and groans
he'll cook you in his dinner pot
your skin, your flesh, your bones
he'll eat your skin and grind your bones
and turn you to a pulp
then swallow you like a pulped egg
gnash, gobble, gulp!

So watch your step when you next go
upon a horrendous stroll,
or you might end up in the pit below
as crunchie for the troll!

Adam Collister (9)
Murray's Road Junior School, Isle of Man

SCHOOL DREAMS!

Miss Fife thinks I'm reading,
but what a big mistake,
I'm sitting on the Milky Way
and eating tea and cake

Mr Coole thinks I'm writing,
but how wrong you are,
I'm lying in space,
stuffing my face
and swinging on a star.

Mrs May thinks I'm listening,
oh no, I'm not,
I'm flying in a rocket
and making a plot.

Miss Cooper thinks I'm painting,
don't be so dumb,
I'm on the planet Jupiter
and have made an alien chum.

'Hello, hello,
is anyone in?
Pay attention my girl,
where have you been?'

Corrine Payne (11)
Murray's Road Junior School, Isle of Man

THE WEREWOLF

Beware of the dangerous werewolf,
Take one step and you're dead meat,
To drag you to his muddy gulf,
He'll make you smell his feet.

His blood is green and freezing cold,
He hits, kicks and punches,
He'll make you big, fat and bold
And eat you for his lunches.

He'll grind your arms and skin your legs
And burn you to a pulp,
Then cover you with pegs,
Grumble, grumble, gulp!

So watch your step when you go,
Around the muddy gulf,
Or you might end up in the bowl below,
As supper for the wolf.

Sam Halpin & Jamie Cubitt (9)
Murray's Road Junior School, Isle of Man

FLYING LIKE A BIRD

Higher and higher,
The wind beneath your wings,
A bird in the sky sings
You know you'll never tire.

The wind whips your hair,
You're high up in the clouds,
Below people watch in crowds,
You are everlasting, like a prayer.

You are an angel in the sky,
The wind has ripped your clothes,
And the marshmallow clouds fill your toes
You are ever so high.

You are flying like a bird,
Up and up you go,
There is no need to swoop low,
Your time is over, you have been heard.

Dannielle Noonan (11)
Murray's Road Junior School, Isle of Man

ONE DAY WITH WINGS

In the air with wings
Flying so high
I feel really dizzy
And I don't know why.

I'm getting chased by a cat
I'm trying to eat my worm
I fly up high, up high on the roof
Then come down to Earth.

I don't know why I'm flying
But I want to go down
To get some worms
For myself.

Katie Norman (10)
Murray's Road Junior School, Isle of Man

OUR WORLD

There are big white clouds up in the sky,
when I look up they're ever so high.
When it rains it makes you sigh,
when it comes down even more
it makes the river high.
When it snows it makes it cold
you must keep warm if you're old.
The wind in the sky
makes the clouds move nearby.
The sun dawns into the sky,
the night comes right up
and the sun is left to die.
When the flowers start to grow
then it sometimes starts to snow.
When the flowers start to die
then the children start to cry.

Emer McCartin (10)
Murray's Road Junior School, Isle of Man

HULLABALOO

A hullabaloo is yellow and blue.
A hullabaloo comes out at night and gives you a fright.
A hullabaloo wears shoes and goes 'Moo!'
A hullabaloo does not like light.
A hullabaloo watches you move.
His teeth are white as glue
And if he does not like you
He will say, *'Boo!'*

Natalie Anderson (9)
Papdale Primary School, Orkney Islands

WHATIF
(Based on 'Whatif' by Shel Silverstein)

Whatif the sky was yellow
whatif the sea was red
whatif the grass turned purple
and then it turned into bread?
Whatif the sun went away
and whatif horses didn't neigh?
Whatif we could not hear
whatif the cheetah couldn't run
and whatif we all weighed a ton?
Whatif we had no fun
whatif the moon was blue
whatif the animals were extinct soon
and all the stars were really small
and there wasn't any Earth at all?
Whatif?

Beverly Campbell (9)
Papdale Primary School, Orkney Islands

HULLABALOO

There was something creeping around
late at night
in our country garden
with sharp teeth
and a
big long neck
that growled.
We screamed and we yelled
we heard a sound
as we shivered
under the covers.
I finally got up
and looked out
and there in the shadows
as I looked down
I laughed
because there I saw
a mouse!

Emma Miller (9)
Papdale Primary School, Orkney Islands

PERFECT DREAMS

I dreamed I was a computer and never froze
I dreamed I was a bike and never had a broken chain.
I dreamed I was a TV and never stopped working.
I dreamed I was a window and never smashed.
I dreamed I was a clock and never gave the wrong time.
I dreamed I was me and never had a peanut allergy.

Miriam Fraser (9)
Papdale Primary School, Orkney Islands

THE STORM

The wind was blowing
The lights were glowing

Everybody was crying with such fright
It was so terrible upon this dark night

The wind was blowing
The lights were glowing

Lightning is coming, home time soon
I am so cold, storm go away before noon

The wind was blowing
The lights were glowing

Things got calmer
The storm was now over.

Shannon Robb (10)
Papdale Primary School, Orkney Islands

BLUE

Blue is the summer sky
filled with singing birds.

Blue is the ocean
shimmering in the sun.

Blue is the sea
lapping on a sandy beach.

Blue is like a jay
gliding through the sky.

Blue is a baby whale
crying for its mum.

Blue is like the band
singing at a concert.

Blue is a dolphin
playing in the sea.

Blue is denim
the jeans I wear.

Blue is the council box
where people put their suggestions.

Blue is an icicle
hanging from my ivy on the house.

Blue is you
feeling cold.

Amy Irvine (10)
Papdale Primary School, Orkney Islands

YELLOW

Yellow is like the sun
it is bright on a summer's day.

Yellow is like pencils
that you write with.

Yellow is like dinner tickets
you hand over to the lady.

Yellow is a paper
good for drawing.

Yellow is like custard
you eat for pudding.

Yellow is a colour of paint
you paint with it.

Yellow is like the medical book
you use when you are hurt.

Yellow is like the project book
you draw in it.

Jennifer Park (10)
Papdale Primary School, Orkney Islands

PEACE

Peace is beauty, woven with thread.
People who've died have gone to their bed.
The sheet of peace if torn then war will rain
Leaving sorrow and pain.
And the people who've left
Will now live in peace

Zoë Matthews (10)
Papdale Primary School, Orkney Islands

BLACK

Black is like burnt toast
that you make in the morning.

Black is like a shadow
that follows you everywhere.

Black is like the crow
that pecks at the scarecrow.

Black is like a bat
very fierce and wild.

Black is like a witch's cat
that wanders on the path.

Black is like your dad's shoe
that he puts on to go to work.

Black are the pupils
right in the corner of the eye.

Calum Ross (10)
Papdale Primary School, Orkney Islands

SILVER

Silver is a salmon
glittering in the sea.

Silver is a ring
that you get at your wedding.

Silver is a five pence
in your money box.

Silver is a life
that you get.

Silver is a medal
shining in the sun.

Silver is the sun
shining up in the sky.

Silver are the stars
away up high.

Silver is a watch
that you bought yesterday.

Silver is a knife
sparkling in the sun.

Silver is rare
it is hard to find.

Silver is a bullet
flying through the air.

Silver!

Eddie Brown (11)
Papdale Primary School, Orkney Islands

THE STORM

The rain felt like a hammer,
Beating against me.
The wind was like a banshee
Screaming in my ear.
The lightning
Was scaring me out of my wits.
The thunder was like monsters
Roaring with the stormy wind.
It was a storm!

Erik Bews (10)
Papdale Primary School, Orkney Islands

BLUE

Blue is like the sky
With lots of clouds.

Blue is like the sea
Crashing against the shore.

Blue is like a bluebell
Ringing in the wind.

Blue is like a book
You read and enjoy.

Blue is like a pencil case
You keep your pencils in.

Blue is like the blue tit
Which wakes you in the morning.

Sheri Allan (10)
Papdale Primary School, Orkney Islands

ONE

Two little rockets blasting off into space
One saw Jupiter and one tied his lace
One saw the moon, one saw the other
One heard a bang, one wanted his mother
One thought it was boring, one thought it was exciting
One thought it was lonely, one thought it was frightening
One was hot, one was cold.
One heard a rattle, one was bold.
One was scared, one was fine.
One said, 'Don't touch the line.'
One saw a planet, one saw stars
One said, 'Hello,' one saw Mars.

Nikita Scollie (10)
Papdale Primary School, Orkney Islands

CURRY

Curry, dear curry,
I love you a lot.
Curry, dear curry,
You're slurpy and hot.
Curry, dear curry,
Your chicken's my best.
I love you, dear curry,
You're covered in sauce.

Curry, oh curry,
You're my favourite meal.
Curry, oh curry,
I love you a lot.
You're spicy and hot.
I love you dear curry,
I can't get enough.
Curry, dear curry,
You're wonderful stuff!

Naomi Armet (9)
Papdale Primary School, Orkney Islands

ALIENS IN SPACE

A liens fly in space.
L ots of aliens laugh at each other.
I cicles are for keeping aliens cool.
E ach time an alien speaks, it echoes.
N ot two eyes. Only one.
S tupid aliens have small heads.

Shannon Dunne (9)
Papdale Primary School, Orkney Islands

SWEETS

Sweets, sweets
I love you so much
You're crunchy, you're soft
I can't get enough.
You're creamy, you're fluffy
Oh how you I adore
Please, just give me loads more.

Sweets, sweets
Piled up high
Almost touching the sky
You're explosive and magic
Juicy and sharp
Is someone playing the harp?
Be quiet, I'm trying to eat!

Ewan Coltherd (9)
Papdale Primary School, Orkney Islands

ALIENS

A liens are large
L ots of eyes
I gloo for a head
E ggs for hands
N inety nostrils
S and for skin.

Shaun Raeburn (9)
Papdale Primary School, Orkney Islands

AN ALIEN

A n alien landed on my roof.
L ay on my bed.
I   thought it was my sister.
E verybody came into my room.
N obody could believe their eyes.

Adam Strutt (8)
Papdale Primary School, Orkney Islands

FEAR

Fear is dark.
It tastes like black liquorice,
And smells like the toilet.
It looks like a moving shadow at night,
And sounds like your heart beating at a high speed.
Fear feels like the hard wet ground.

Greg Rendall (11)
Papdale Primary School, Orkney Islands

SADNESS

Sadness is black.
It tastes like soggy cornflakes
and smells like a rotten flower.
It looks like an old person risen from the dead
and sounds like stairs creaking and moaning.
Sadness feels like a hole in your heart that never heals up.

Alice Rendall (11)
Papdale Primary School, Orkney Islands

PLAYGROUND

The noise of people shouting
Footballs going everywhere
Whistles blowing
People laughing
Some falling
Others arguing
In the cold, cold playground, all alone.

Ryan Taylor (8)
Papdale Primary School, Orkney Islands

PLAYGROUND

Playground
is fun
and noisy.
Running as fast
as you can.
Happiness and
sadness.
Fun and games,

but now we have
to go in.

Sally Laughton (8)
Papdale Primary School, Orkney Islands

ALIENS

A   liens have purple and yellow skin.
L   ots of spots on them.
I   ntelligent little aliens.
E   veryone gets scared.
N   ine legs on them
S   tronger than big men.

Rebecca Coates (8)
Papdale Primary School, Orkney Islands

WHATIF
(Based on 'Whatif' by Shel Silverstein)

Whatif the sea was yellow?
Whatif people did bellow?
Whatif the sun was blue?
Whatif there wasn't me and you?
Whatif there was no light?
Whatif there was no night?
Whatif there was no day?

It's hard for me to say
whatif there was no moon?
Whatif a meteor came soon?
Whatif there was no sun?
There wouldn't be any fun.

Ewan Mackay (9)
Papdale Primary School, Orkney Islands

BORING OLD TREE
(Haiku)

Swaying in the wind
Staying there in all seasons
Casting off your leaves.

John Waters (10)
Papdale Primary School, Orkney Islands

SEASIDE
(Haiku)

Sun by the seaside,
The ice cream cones are melting
Because it's so hot.

Danna Wilson (10)
Papdale Primary School, Orkney Islands

ALIENS

A   liens are all sorts of colours
L   egs on their heads
I   ce cream cones for ears
E   ight eyes
N   ine legs
S   ix arms.

Erin Flett (8)
Papdale Primary School, Orkney Islands

DRAGON
(Haiku)

My dragon is cool
He snores when he goes to bed
My dragon hates you!

Kerri Cameron (10)
Papdale Primary School, Orkney Islands

HOLIDAY
(Haiku)

Holidays are great.
Sliding down a water slide.
Never want to leave.

Katy Berston (11)
Papdale Primary School, Orkney Islands

DRAGON
(Haiku)

Dragons have glasses
My dragon is different
It reads books at night.

Ryan Norquoy (11)
Papdale Primary School, Orkney Islands

DRAGON
(Haiku)

Flying in the air
He will give you a big scare . . .
When he lands on you!

James Seatter (11)
Papdale Primary School, Orkney Islands

DRAGON
(Haiku)

I am small and smart
I play with my small round rocks
I am not friendly.

Steven Windwick (10)
Papdale Primary School, Orkney Islands

SNOW IS THE WEATHER

Snow is the weather
That children want to last all year round
When the snow covers all of the ground
At the rising of the sun
The children have lots of fun
They want to play and play
To the end of the day
Snow is the weather
That children want to last all year round.

Ryan Kemp (10)
Papdale Primary School, Orkney Islands

DEEP AND CRISPY MORNING

The crispy sound
As you set down your feet,
The crackle and crunch,
Oh how I love the sound,
On a beautiful crispy day,
When the robin shines out his little red breast,
He goes, 'Tweet, tweet.'
On a deep and crispy morning.

Megan Foulis (9)
Papdale Primary School, Orkney Islands

THE SEASONS

Spring is when baby animals are born,
The buds on the trees are now in flower.

Summer is when the sun is hot
Leaves are bright green.

Autumn is when the leaves are brown and crispy
Falling on the ground.

Winter is the time when the snow falls
All around is white.

Karen Laughton (10)
Papdale Primary School, Orkney Islands

WE DON'T CARE

When the snow falls
It builds up high
I go outside and run around.

When the rain falls
It melts the snow

When the sun shines
It dries the rain

When the ice comes
We slide around

We don't care what weather it is
We all go out and have lots of fun.

Carolynn Leslie (10)
Papdale Primary School, Orkney Islands

THE WEATHER

When the sun shines
children run and play

When the wind blows
it blows things away

When the snow falls
it covers everything with
a white blanket of snow

When the sun shines
it melts the snow

When the rain falls
it makes puddles on the ground

When the sun comes out again
it dries up the puddles
and the children run and play again.

Fiona Eunson (9)
Papdale Primary School, Orkney Islands

WHEN THE SNOW FALLS

When the snow falls
down and down
silently, silently, come
the clouds!

When the snow falls
more and more
hard on your ears
hard on your toes

When the snow falls
cold and soft
cold as ice
soft as fluff.

Jordan Yarrow (10)
Papdale Primary School, Orkney Islands

CANDLES

Light blazing beautifully
Flame glowing brightly
Light reflecting pleasantly
Flame dancing wonderfully
Wax melting happily
Wick smoking pleasantly

Amy Kerr (9)
Papdale Primary School, Orkney Islands

THE GREAT ANIMAL CHARGE

Animals thumping
Animals snorting
Animals making so many noises
Animals snapping
Animals munching
Animals making such a noise
What a hullabaloo!

Claire McCreath (9)
Papdale Primary School, Orkney Islands

MISHAP AT MUSIC CLASS

Trumpets *honk*,
Pianos *jangle*,
Violins *crack*,
Harps *twang*,
Bells *bong*,
Drums *boom*,
Kids *run*,
Teacher *yells*,
What a hullabaloo!

Astrid Nicolson (9)
Papdale Primary School, Orkney Islands

TORNADO

It's a tornado!
Twisting dust
Twirling houses
Whistling wind
Run, run into the shelter!
What a hullabaloo!

Erin Watts (10)
Papdale Primary School, Orkney Islands

VOLCANO EXPLOSION!

Erupting volcano
Hissing gases
Crackling rocks
Blazing lava
Wonderful colours
Burning hot
What a hullabaloo!

Jenna Hamilton (9)
Papdale Primary School, Orkney Islands

BOILING HOT VOLCANOES

Blazing lava
hissing gases
crackling rocks
booming voices
erupting volcanoes
run, run for shelter
here comes boiling hot lava.
What a hullabaloo!

Tina Griffiths (10)
Papdale Primary School, Orkney Islands

ANIMAL HULLABALOO

Dogs growling
Birds singing
Cats howling
Monkeys swinging

Cows mooing
Lions *roaring*
Owls hooting
Eagles soaring.

Laura Robertson (10)
Papdale Primary School, Orkney Islands

HULLABALOO

It's raining and all my washing's still outside!
'Tabby cat! Tabby cat!
Come back in, it's starting to pour.
Sammy! Sammy!
Come back here! It's raining.

Run for it! You'll be soaked to the bone!
Aagh! Thunder!
Help me! Somebody!
It's rumbling in my ear like an earthquake.'

Night-time. Everybody's tucked up in bed.
Inside their homes, snuggled up by the fire.
No more rain. The storm's over.
What a hullabaloo!

Kirsten Jamieson (10)
Quarff Primary School, Shetland Islands

HULLABALOO

T   rucks, vans and cars bonking their horns
R   oger the baby trying to sleep
A   nimals in cars want to know what's happening
F   iremen and police calming people down
F   urious adults shouting at each other
I   mpossible to get out since that truck's broken
C   an't get that truck to move again

J   ust another hour 'til we get it cleared
A   nd even the school bus is in the middle of this
M   ums and dads worrying about their kids

S   tadium's expecting their footballers
T   erribly bored children sulking
R   emoving that truck is taking a while
E   ventually they move it
E   verybody's happy
T   hanks for waiting.

Dawn Smith (11)
Quarff Primary School, Shetland Islands

85

THE ICE CREAM VAN

I love the ice cream van
It comes every hour
It has the best ice cream
And it has some kind of power!

On hot days, the van
Is my best friend,
Plus the ice cream man is cool
He wears the latest trends.

But one day the van didn't come!
Everyone was standing outside, looking glum.
Come on ice cream van, my chum!

They all started fussing about
How hot they all were
And how they were dripping with sweat!
And if the ice cream van man didn't come,
They'd all give him a terrible threat.

Some kids started crying,
They said that they were dying.
And the only thing that I can say is
'What a hullabaloo!'

Lisa Manson (11)
Quarff Primary School, Shetland Islands

OCEANA

Oceana, Australia to you and me,
they live their life in harmony.
With snakes and spiders, deadly too
their spiders live under the loo.
Their snakes live in confined spaces
so they can live in many places.
They have lots of other animals too,
like the kangaroo,
With one kick they could kill you!

There are safer animals too
like the koala but not the kangaroo,
The koala is so laid back, it spends its day
eating and sleeping.
The wallaby spends his day peeping.

Birds fly high as the sun
fly higher and higher, till the day has gone.
So Oceana, Australia to you and me
they live their life in harmony.

Glenn Watterson (11)
Rushen Primary School, Isle of Man

WHATEVER THE WEATHER

Whatever the weather
It's best not to wear leather
If the wind is blowing
On the mountain, it's snowing
When the weather man says, 'Heavy rain!'
You should find it splashes on the windowpane
If you're sailing in a yacht and the wind is blowing a gale
You have no choice but to be sick over the rail
So remember next time the weather has gone crazy
Stay in bed and be lazy.

Glenn Buckley (11)
Rushen Primary School, Isle of Man

BIRDS

Birds every day, in every way
Bluebirds, blackbirds,
Thin birds, fat birds
Birds at the beach
Birds in the park
Some in the light
Some in the dark
Some eating nuts
Some eating bread
Some alive,
Some dead
Some fly high
Some fly low.

Gemma Toher (11)
Rushen Primary School, Isle of Man

HIP HOP AUNT

There was a hip hop aunt
Who had a pet ant
Who hopped all day
To the beat of the DJ
They hopped to the loo
They hopped to their bed.
They are that mad they painted the town red.
Remember there was a hip hop aunt
Who had a little ant!

Emily Kelsall (11)
Rushen Primary School, Isle of Man

KANGAROO BOXER

The kangaroo boxer is so strong,
When he farts, it's such a pong.
He will thump you, if you thump him
He will thump you in the limb.

The kangaroo boxer is so strong,
His tail is incredibly long.
If he hits you, you will cry,
You are lucky if you don't die.

The kangaroo boxer is so strong,
He can sing a classical song.
If he trips you, you will fall,
The kangaroo boxer is so tall.

Michael Craine (10)
Rushen Primary School, Isle of Man

AGENT ELEPHANT

He's our best agent
But he's going to get an engagement
You cannot miss 'im
Take my advice do not diss him
If you're bad, you will regret
Because he's a threat
He's Snowy, the elephant agent
Who's going to get an engagement.

James Casizzi (11)
Rushen Primary School, Isle of Man

RUGBY GORILLA

There's a gorilla who plays rugby
From his feet the grass gets smudgy.
All his team are types of apes
All his team are good mates
He's a team captain
He does all the ranting
All he likes is winning
That's why he does loads of sprinting
But one day -
All the team ran away
Then the gorilla was all alone.

Adam Brown (10)
Rushen Primary School, Isle of Man

FISH EVERYWHERE

Fish are in the sea, fish are in the pond
Fish are orange, fish are yellow, they are all colours.
Fish swim, swim, swim all day long, under the deep blue sea.
Fish are eating bread, fish are eating loads of things all day long.
But at the end of the day, there is only one person coming to get them
Shark!
The shark is in the sea, the shark is hungry,
Hungry as he can be, munch, munch, munch all day long.
Mmmm this is very yummy. Fish are my best thing
To eat when I'm really, really, really hungry
I need fish to eat!
The fish have friends, lots and lots of friends.
Fish have only one best friend and they are jellyfish.
Fish have lots and lots of friends but they all have a worst enemy
and that's the shark.
They certainly don't want to make friends with him because
he's a nasty man to play with. *Oh yeah!*

Lana Cowell (11)
Rushen Primary School, Isle of Man

KITTY

Last night I brought a mouse in,
My owner screamed and screamed.
I didn't think she'd be this excited
But then she told me off.
Then the other human woke up
And came down the stairs.
She hugged me tight and sobbed into my fur.
'Oh Kitty, how could you? That poor little mouse!'
Then she put me down and patted my head,
I went running one way and she went the other.
Eew! she got my fur all wet
I mean, sheesh, I'm a cat!

Jennifer Caley (10)
Rushen Primary School, Isle of Man

UNCLE'S VOYAGES

My uncle has a boat,
He sails it everywhere, even in a moat,
The boat's as smelly as a welly,
And is called the Pig's Belly.

Yesterday he went to the Amazon
And caught a salmon
But where to now?
Ooops, I hit the bow.

It's very exciting,
Sailing across the Atlantic,
Sail the seven seas
But try not to go under the sea.

My uncle has a boat,
The boat's full of *hullabaloo!*
Ooooooooooo!
You might find treasure.
Are you sure?

John Maclean (11)
Sandwickhill School, Isle of Lewis

THE HULLABALOO ROLLER COASTER

Noisy it was, really noisy.
It was the biggest one I had seen yet,
People were screaming while on it
And others were closing their eyes.
Everyone was excited - but scared.

Kayleigh Fraser (11)
Sandwickhill School, Isle of Lewis

HULLABALOO

Having fun
Making noise
Laughing, cheering, singing . . .
Hullabaloo!

We're causing noise,
Singing cheerfully.
Playing games
Causing a riot
Hullabaloo!

Screaming, shouting,
Yelling, screeching.

Hush now, here comes my mum.
Sees my room -
Hullabaloo!

Eilidh Campbell Morrison (11)
Sandwickhill School, Isle of Lewis

PARTY

H aving a party is really cool,
U p and down, jumping around.
L aughing with all your friends,
L oving every minute of it,
A nd dancing the night away.
B lazing music
A nd having fun.
L ook at the time, we've got to go.
O oooohhh no!
O oooohhh no!

Claire Margaret Macleod (11)
Sandwickhill School, Isle of Lewis

HULLABALOO!

Riding side to side, up, down!
Over, under, darker, darker!
Level out. I'm going to be sick!
'Let me off this rattle of metal!' all the grans will say.
'Everyone off, or pay again!' the boss will say.
'Ride it! Ride it! Only £3!'
'Can I? Can I?' all the kids will ask
'No!' some will reply.

'Oh why not try our awesome new ride
And pay £3, that's fine!'
'Stacey, hurry up, I want to go on this ride!'

'Today, only the big ride!' the boss will say.
Everyone come, oh please, come on this ride.
Ready or not! Have you guessed what I am?

Kerri Louise Macdonald (11)
Sandwickhill School, Isle of Lewis

HULLABALOO

Riding up and down hills
Cycling on the path
Getting faster and faster
I might end up in a crash
Watching out for cars
I'd better be careful
I'm trying to pull the brakes
But the bike just shakes.

Daniel Smith (11)
Sandwickhill School, Isle of Lewis

HULLABALOO

Every starry night I get ready
for my flight,
To space, for my big race,
To get away from all
the pollution.
In this year, I hope there will be
no smoke coming out of cars,
'Cause if there is -
We will all choke.

Paul Smith (11)
Sandwickhill School, Isle of Lewis

FIRE

Fire, fire keep away
Don't try to be a hero
Settle for a zero
Get help, don't try
to *save* what you can.
Leave as fast as you can.
Specialists will do the job,
Get out of the house -
I mean it, stay out!
Fire kills!

James MacRae (10)
Scalpay School, Isle of Harris

GOD'S LOVE

God loves little girls,
More than precious pearls,
Deaf, dumb, disabled or lame,
God loves them all, just the same.

God loves little boys,
He watches over them, playing with their toys,
God has a lovely promise to keep,
He'll watch over them, awake or asleep.

God loves the old,
More than precious gold.
He'll stay by forever
So you'll always be together.

God loves the responsible and young,
Sing praises to God with your tongue.
If you can't sing, sing in your heart,
Sing praises to God and take part.

God has a lovely promise to keep,
To stay with you when the road is steep
And if you believe in Him,
He will save you from your sins.

Laura MacSween (10)
Scalpay School, Isle of Harris

SCHOOL

School's cool on Mondays
At 1.45pm, we go to the canteen
Also people say things they don't mean
That's one day.

School's okay on Tuesdays
We do home economics
We sew and make things
Also we bake things.

School's good on Wednesdays
That's why I'm not in a mood
We draw and paint and others
Even though we don't paint mothers.

School's boring on Thursdays
We just do French and sing
But we have to watch in case the bees sting
In summer, outside.

School's great on Fridays
Especially after lunch
We don't munch crisps
We sing and play instruments.

That's my week at school
Sometimes it's good and sometimes it's bad
We sometimes have fun and
We sometimes run.

Donna Marie Morrison (10)
Scalpay School, Isle of Harris

THE GINGERBREAD MAN

Golden brown is he
As crunchy as a bee
As small as a dwarf
And as warm as a scarf.

He runs for his life
As soon as he sees the knife
His leg is already off
And his crumbs will make you cough.

Soon the baker has caught him
As his eyes go dim
A boy comes in
And he isn't thin.

Iain MacLennan (11)
Scalpay School, Isle of Harris

MILLIE MY PET DOG

Millie is my dog's name,
In the living room she plays a ball game,
Little dog, she was before
Little dog, not any more.
Idiotic she is sometimes
Every day, her eyes look like dimes.

Millie has a ball which is ripped up
Yellow or blue ball, she will throw it up.

Pink tongue and black coat
Everything I have wrote
True it is.

Dark brown eyes and a long nose
On her head, everyone knows
Go to bed now Millie.

Kevin MacLeod (11)
Scalpay School, Isle of Harris

MY HAMSTER

I have a hamster.
His name is Tipsy.
He's really neat.
He likes to nibble on my toys' feet.
He's brown and white.
He stays up at night.
He's cute and cuddly.
He will eat anything.
Even me!

Lauren MacSween (8)
Scalpay School, Isle of Harris

It's Lucky

It's lucky we have the police
Or robbers would get away
It's lucky we have nurses and doctors
Or we would hurt all day
It's lucky we have the fire brigade
Or your house would be on fire
It's lucky we have all those
To keep us safe and well.

Derek MacKenzie (8)
Scalpay School, Isle of Harris

FIREWORKS NIGHT

Bang, bang, boom, boom! If I run
any further, I'll run out of room.
My fur's on end, my tail's in the air,
Every time they set off a firework,
it gives me a scare.
I think of my basket, all cosy and warm,
Why couldn't they just have left me at home -
Instead of leaving me out to roam?

Andrew La Hay (10)
Shapinsay Primary School, Isle of Orkney

HIGH WAVES

H igh, the waves are
I n the ocean sea
G oing wild the waves are
H igh in the sea

W aves are going higher
A nd there'll be a storm
V iolent waves are crashing
E ndless waves are breaking
S kies become calm, the storm is dead.

Helen Le-Mar (10)
Shapinsay Primary School, Isle of Orkney

THE HULLABALOO FROG

H ullabaloo frog hops over mountains and swims
U nder oceans
L upa hoop! Lupa hoop! Is his call.
L upa-hoopa is his favourite song
A nd gold is his favourite colour
B arbecued newts are his favourite meal
A nts in cream for dessert
L ike his brothers, he lives in a mystical palace
O f gold and silver which over centuries, has been coated with a spell
O f hullabaloo magic.

Craig Horton (10)
Shapinsay Primary School, Isle of Orkney

I TRIED TO WRITE A POEM

I tried to write a poem
Instead of doing maths,
The poem was such rubbish
I threw it in the trash.

For every line I wrote
I saw it wouldn't do
And as for rhyming verses
I haven't got a clue.

The bin began to fill
And my head began to swim
My pencil was all blunt
So I tried to write . . . a hymn!

Patrick McMaster (11)
Shiskine Primary School, Isle of Arran

THE LONELY CHILD

The lonely child is walking around
Just waiting to be found
No friends to play with
The rain is pouring
The birds are snoring
Waiting for some company.

He sits in his hood
No wonder he's in a mood
Because he is alone.

So he walks along
Now he hears a song
It is children
They come towards him
Wanting him to play
On this lovely day
Now he's not sad
And things are not so bad
He has finally got company!

Ben Young (11)
Shiskine Primary School, Isle of Arran

THE CAT

The cat is sleek and shiny
and prowls from tree to tree
and when the mice are running by
it pounces proudly.
When the cat is prowling proudly
it hides behind the trees.
It tiptoes along the paths
and looks suspiciously
for its prey.
When the days dawn and
the sun has gone from the sky
and there's nothing
to be seen except from
the cat's eyes.
Quickly and quietly the cat
runs back inside and curls
up into a ball, until the next morning
when another big adventure will begin!

Jennifer Ingham (11)
Shiskine Primary School, Isle of Arran

CORAL REEFS

Amazing fishes, colourful and bright
You can even see them when it's dark at night,
Colourful coral in the deep blue sea
It is the most amazing place to be.
Lots of dolphins in great big schools
I think this place is really cool,
The precious urchins, seaweed and shells
Sometimes if you shake them they sound like bells.
The electric eels lying in the sand
Waiting to shake someone who touches them with their hand.
The razor-sharp teeth on the great white shark
And dogfishes which you think might bark.
Big boxer jellyfish, which I don't like very much
Can kill a grown man with one single touch.
An octopus squirting its powerful ink
The sharks can eat you in just one blink
The blue whale, he's the leader of them all
If you stood him up, he'd be twenty-six metres tall.
The mystery of the shipwrecks and treasure lying there
The fantasy of the reef is just *everywhere!*

Eilidh Kerr (11)
Shiskine Primary School, Isle of Arran

MY LITTLE BROTHER

Liam, my little brother
Climbs all round the room
He's like a piece of rubber
But after a while . . . *boom!*

Hopefully, he's not dead
He's lying on the floor,
He's fallen and hurt his head
He hit it on the door.

We take him down the lane
To see the clever doctor
He was in awful pain
So we jumped into a helicopter.

We reached the hospital far away,
The doctor examined his head
He told him jumping was not good play
Or he'd stay forever in bed.

The doctor carried out one more test
And said nothing was wrong,
Liam had been an awful pest
And faked it all along!

Madelaine Gruber (10)
Shiskine Primary School, Isle of Arran

BESIDE THE SEA

Beside the sea there was
a bumblebee,
And the bumblebee, he sat
beside me,
beside the sea.
The bumblebee flew up to the tree
which stood beside me,
Below the tree which
stood beside me.
A crab crawled along
as cute as could be,
He played in the sand
then sat on my hand,
Under the tree which
stood beside me.
We played there for hours
great friends we would be,
Down by the seaside,
under our tree.

Nicola Currie (9)
Shiskine Primary School, Isle of Arran

WHAT IS A FRIEND?

A friend . . . is someone nice
A friend . . . is someone you can share feelings with
A friend . . . is someone you have things in common with
A friend . . . is someone you can share secrets with.

A friend . . . will always be there for you
A friend . . . will always care for you
A friend . . . will always help you, no matter what.

A friend . . . will never lie to you
A friend . . . will never leave you out
A friend . . . will never hurt you.

A friend . . . is all these things and more.

Yasmin Nazary (11)
Shiskine Primary School, Isle of Arran

MARTIANS TOOK MY BROTHER MIM

Martians took my brother Mim
I wonder what they want with him?
He picks his nose and cheats at pool
(That Martian leader is a fool!).
They went through Mars and Mim yelled, '*Mum!*
I need some food down in my tum!'
They fed him Pluto porridge and Spangled Star spaghetti
They prodded and they poked him and thought he was a yeti!
Mim got mad, the leader sad
So they whisked him home that night.
They landed in the garden and gave Mum and Dad a fright.
'Is it chips for tea tonight?' asked Mim,
The journey didn't bother him!

Ciaran McMaster (9)
Shiskine Primary School, Isle of Arran

SEASONS

S   pring has come with the daffodils
P   laces full of dancing yellow
R   ain will come, sparkling over the world
I   nside! To search for umbrellas.
N   ow that it has stopped. Ho! Ho! Outside to play
G   ame's good! No time to stop! Let's run and play.

S   un has come, get outside to play,
U   nder the sun we stay till the moon comes overhead
M   aybe we should go to the beach?
M   aybe we will get an ice cream?
E   ven if we don't, we still have fun
R   un around, have a laugh.

A   utumn has come
U   sually down to the machair
T   here is too much to be done
U   nder the corn to hide from work
M   any bags of potatoes to pick
N   ever a rest, just work, work, work.

W   inter has come with its icy cold weather
I   nside! Hurry! You might get cold.
N   ow you are inside at a cosy fire,
T   he grass hard with frost.
E   veryone waiting for Santa,
R   ound your neck, wear your scarf to go outside.

Alana MacInnes (10)
Stoneybridge Primary School, Isle of South Uist

SONGS

Listening to the radio and the songs that it plays,
Brings me to life, counting the days.
Laughing my head off or singing along.
I know it's good, because I wrote it.
It's hard for me to dance along,
Because this is a complicated song.
While I've got the song in my head,
My mum shouts out that it's time for bed.
While I snuggle down in my bed, I hum.
Next morning, my song has gone.

Mairi Sarah MacRury (10)
Stoneybridge Primary School, Isle of South Uist

NOBODY IS NORMAL

Nobody is normal or strange
Everybody is different in their own way
Some people might be a bit unfair
By laughing at the colour of your hair.
It doesn't matter if you're fat or thin
It doesn't matter about melanin.
It shouldn't matter if you're fat or thin . . .
We should live together
In a good community
With no racism.

Sheldon Muchmore (11)
Whalsay School, Shetland Islands

RED ROCKET

Red rocket
On a stick
If it shines
Lick it quick
Round the edges
On the top
Round the bottom
Don't stop.
Suck the lolly
Lick your lips
Lick the sides
As it drips
Quick! Quick!
Lick! Lick!
Before it drips.

Mhairi Stewart (11)
Whalsay School, Shetland Islands

THIS THING CALLED RACISM

I want to live in a community without
This thing called racism,
I would do anything to get rid of
This thing called racism
I hate *this thing called racism.*
Everybody should hate
This thing called racism.
It makes me sick
This thing called racism.
Nobody is different
This thing called racism.
It's a waste of time
This thing called racism.
Nobody is perfect, nobody is normal
I think you get my point, now!

Mari Irvine (11)
Whalsay School, Shetland Islands

RACISM

We wouldn't like to live in a community
With this word *racism*
It would be unfair to use this word *racism.*
It is a bad word racism, it can't help people be friends.
It would make friends become enemies.

Liam Williamson (11)
Whalsay School, Shetland Islands

WHY?

Why are people racist?
Why do they abuse others?
Why do they care about skin colour?
Why should they criticise your looks?
Why should they judge you by your size?
Why are they nasty if you're disabled?
Why don't they think about other people's feelings?
Why?

Laura Ann Kay (11)
Whalsay School, Shetland Islands

WHY?

Do you scare because you don't care?
Are you prejudiced, because you never listen?
Do you bully for fun and games?
Is it unfair that you judge the book by its cover?
Why do you not read it?
Why can't we talk it over and not argue?
Why can't we all be friends instead of enemies?
Why do people have to be racist?
What community do you want to live in?
Should we have a kind, nice and helpful community,
Or a nasty, horrible, thieving community?
Why do we care about things like this?
All I need to know is *why?*

Vicky Anne Irvine (11)
Whalsay School, Shetland Islands

SHOULD BEING DIFFERENT MAKE ANY DIFFERENCE?

Should being different
Make any difference?
If someone moves
To your island
And they are
A different colour
Short or tall
Should that make a difference?
Should you bully them?
If you moved there,
Would you like them
To bully you?

David Williamson (11)
Whalsay School, Shetland Islands

NOBODY'S PERFECT

Racism is very bad,
Only for people who are sad.
It doesn't matter if they are Japanese
Or even if they are Chinese.
Don't bully people because they are tall
Or if they are small.
Nobody's normal, nobody's perfect.
So why *racism?*

Neil Polson (11)
Whalsay School, Shetland Islands

ALIENS RULE!

Aliens
Green and gooey,
Do they live on Mars or Neptune?
I'd like to go up there,
To meet an alien!
It would be great fun
Play with them all day
And try on pink, fluffy dresses.
That's all I've got to say
About aliens.

Shelley Sandison
Whalsay School, Shetland Islands

MERSEYSIDE DERBY

It was a wet soggy day
In the middle of May
When the Merseyside Derby was played

The first half of the match
Was a bit of a snatch
But then a free kick was made

Rooney potted the ball in
With a bit of a spin
So the Toffees went on to victory

Well five months later
A Liverpool hater
Heard Rooney was moving to Liverpool
But what he did was not cruel
He actually stuck up his thumb!
So from that day till now
There's never been a row
When the Merseyside Derby's been played.

Joe McElhone (11)
Whalsay School, Shetland Islands

MY DREAM COMMUNITY

My dream community,
Is a peaceful one.
A community without racism,
To some people it is just a dream.
To some people racism
Is just a joke.
Racism to others
Is something that is a lifetime of misery.

My dream community,
Is one where everyone is friendly,
A community without vandalism
Would be fantastic.
So far this dream community
Is sadly just a dream.

Kristina Eunson
Whalsay School, Shetland Islands

RIVERS

Rivers round the world are different
Some rivers are rough, raging, swirling, violent and enormous.
Others are quiet, calm and lovely,
These are the rivers that made that frown, upside down.
The rivers that are dangerous, rough and terrible,
Makes that smile upside down, in other words a big, bad frown!
Some rivers are beautiful, sparkling and dazzling,
All in one!

Tammi Anderson (9)
Whalsay School, Shetland Islands

MY HOUSE

My house has a bedroom
With lots of books.
If we go down the stairs
The first room we come to is the sitting room.
If we go and sit down on the sofa,
There's a light, so we're not in the dark.
In the kitchen there're pots and pans
On the table there is really yummy food.
Beside the table there's a computer
To help us find out things.

Greg Anderson (8)
Whalsay School, Shetland Islands

SPORTS

I play football, it is hard
You have to run fast
I like kicking the ball hard
It is fun
Tennis is good too
I can hit the ball very far
I like playing tennis with Bobby
It is fun
I love badminton
I play it lots of the time
I play in the Leisure Centre
They are a hard net in the middle
of the racket
It is fun too
I don't really like netball
It is for girls
Squash is sort of good,
The ball is squishy.
I play volleyball all the time
You have to have a hard fist.

Steven Thompson (9)
Whalsay School, Shetland Islands

ANIMALS

I love animals
Big elephants making big noises
Small mice making small noises
Spotty cheetahs running really fast
Orange lions growling at people
Green snakes hissing at one another
White polar bears eating fish
Stripy dogs rolling in the gutter
Long giraffes with really long necks
Short beetles which are black
Fat ostriches looking for food
Thin cats, really hungry
Helpless cubs with their mum.

Sarah Polson (9)
Whalsay School, Shetland Islands

MY MAGNIFICENT DOG

Water in its bowl
Dog food in its kennel,
Grass it sniffs.
Thin ears
Fat tail,
Spotty back,
Happy face.
Hairy legs,
Dirty nose,
Fluffy body.
Small eyes and
Big toes.

John Laurence Irvine (9)
Whalsay School, Shetland Islands

MY DOG

My dog is spotty
Stripes on its face
Black on its tail
White on its back
Grey on its tummy
Taller than a skyscraper
Long and stretchy
And eats nothing.

Valerie Sales (8)
Whalsay School, Shetland Islands

MY CAT AND HER KITTENS

Cats are fat and skinny
But not like my cat.
My cat is toffee coloured
With little pink paws.
She is very cute.
Her name is Fudge.
She is silly with you.
She even has some kittens!
They are black ones, white ones,
Skinny ones, fat ones, huge ones.
Some of them are white.
They are very nice.
The black ones are bad!
They make me mad!
Well, that is my cat and kittens
Oh no! They're chewing my mittens!

Lynda Hutchison (10)
Whalsay School, Shetland Islands

FOOTBALL

The ball goes soaring
It flies in the net
I kick it hard
Over your head
The ball goes to your feet
I wear football boots with special studs
We bend it in the top corner
Each player has a number
You run up the pitch.

Steve Pottinger (10)
Whalsay School, Shetland Islands

LIZARDS

I like lizards
Tall and sometimes small.
Some are fat, some are flat,
Some are thin and medium.
I like their colours,
Especially blue like the sea
And some are fast,
Some are slow
Because their body is very low.
Some eat meat
And some are vegetarian,
They like digging for food,
They like leaping to eat dragonflies,
Some even eat fish from rivers and streams,
Some climb trees to get away
Or to get fruit to eat,
I like lizards.

Tom Hutchison (9)
Whalsay School, Shetland Islands

OUTSIDE

Outside I see a volcano, it is hot and is about to erupt,
I see the sea, rough and cool
'Mum, I want to go in.'
'No, it's too cold for you.'
'Hey, there's some trees, I want to go climb them.'
'No, they're too high for you.'
'I'll go and pluck some plants for you.'
'OK, go outside and go to the rose bush.'
'OK Mum, there's the rose bush.'
'Here you go.'
'Oh, look at all those colours, pink, red and blue.'

Holly Ann Jamieson (8)
Whalsay School, Shetland Islands

NOBODY'S NORMAL

Nobody's normal, nobody's strange
Humans come in a wide range
Shape doesn't matter, not fat nor thin
Nor does the colour of melanin
Your language doesn't really matter
Nor does the dialect in which you chatter.

Nobody's normal, nobody's strange
Really we're all just the same
Humans are humans
Just the same
And it doesn't matter what is your name.

Richie Hutchison (11)
Whalsay School, Shetland Islands

THE LIFE OF A LEAF

You may think that leaves are boring,
You may even start snoring:
But if you think for quite some time
You could make sense of my rhyme.

First of all they go bright green
That can be pretty for all who have seen
Secondly they go brown and gold
But that's just a sign of leaves getting old.

Last thing of all is very dramatic:
Loads of the leaves get blown in your attic
And from the trees the leaves do fall
That is when the children call.

Leah Whysall (9)
Willaston Primary School, Isle of Man

DEATH

Like a big black hole in the ground.
Men firing guns everywhere.
Nails down a blackboard.
Like daggers in your head.
Like blood on a stone.
Gone in Hell.

Luke Callister (9)
Willaston Primary School, Isle of Man

MY BIKE

I'm taking my bike out to play,
On a nice sunny day.
My seat is padded and comfy
It isn't even lumpy.

I'm zooming, rushing around the street,
On my bike using both of my feet.

Using my hamburger shaped bell
To move the lazy cats, sat in the road
Instead of on mats.

My bike is shiny and really cool,
In Year 6 I'll be able to take it to school.
But until then I'm happy to ride
With my friend Hayley, side by side.

Amy Sharpe (9)
Willaston Primary School, Isle of Man

LOVE

Is like a butterfly dancing in the sky
Is like two birds singing in a tree
As smooth as a silky gown
Is like a chocolate heart melting in my mouth
Like a rosebud on a summer's day
Lives at the bottom of the heart.

Lauren Reed (10)
Willaston Primary School, Isle of Man

LOVE

Is like a butterfly dancing in the moonlight,
Is like two birds singing in a tree,
As smooth as a silky gown,
Is like a chocolate heart melting in your mouth,
Is like rosebuds on a summer's day,
Lives at the bottom of the heart.

Rachel Simpson (10)
Willaston Primary School, Isle of Man

SNOW

Silently and softly the ghostly white snow
Sneaks down from the air.
No one knows when it will come again,
Other people play snowballs and snowmen,
When I get home I will build a snowman.

Samantha Hurd (10)
Willaston Primary School, Isle of Man

Death

Looks like an angel dancing up in Heaven
And devils saying, 'Shut up!'
Looks like a person getting killed and it feels scary.
Looks like blood dripping off someone.
Looks like blood on a rock.
Lives in the middle of a bullet.

Mark Quirk (10)
Willaston Primary School, Isle of Man

LOVE

Is nice and soft like a teddy bear
Rustles like the leaves in the morning air
Is nice and soft
Is like cotton
Is like wool

And it lives on my bed.

Jack Divers (10)
Willaston Primary School, Isle of Man

LOVE

Is two people together forever
Is the ringing bells of Heaven
Is the softness of the rainbow
Is romance floating in the air
Is sweet and sour
Lives in the middle of your heart.

Natasha Younger (10)
Willaston Primary School, Isle of Man

STRESS

Is pale and stretched,
Is like moaning and groaning,
Is jagged and rough,
Is bitter and mouldy,
Is hot and burning,
Lives in the energy of man.

Emily Platten (8)
Willaston Primary School, Isle of Man

DEATH

Is like a big black blob in front of your eyes.
It's like lava from a volcano.
It is like an earthquake just erupting.
It is like a red-hot fire.
It is like dust from ashes
And lives in a murderer's heart.

Peter Keig (9)
Willaston Primary School, Isle of Man

DEATH

Is like a fireball,
Is like screaming people,
Is like smooth blood,
Is red-hot chilli peppers,
Is like gas,
Lives down in Hell.

Chris Craine & Nathan Quilliam (9)
Willaston Primary School, Isle of Man

DEATH

Is like a big black blob in front of your eyes.
It's like lava from a volcano.
It is like an earthquake just erupting.
It is like a red-hot fire.
It is like ashes from a dusty fire
And lives in a murderer's heart.

Stephanie Watson (8)
Willaston Primary School, Isle of Man

STRESS

Stress looks like a sort of pale colour and stretched.
It is like moaning and groaning.
It is jagged and rough.
It is bitter and mouldy.
It is hot and burning.
It lives in the energy of a man.

Sam Okell (9)
Willaston Primary School, Isle of Man

THE BEAR

I had a polar bear on my bed
I had a polar bear under my head
Please stay by the light
Please stay by the light
Please stay at night
Please stay the night
Please don't fear
Please don't fright
Please stay with me
Until the moonlight shines bright.

Kirren Watkinson (9)
Willaston Primary School, Isle of Man